Make it easy...
English
Quick Tests

Age 9-10

Louis Fidge

Test 1 Synonyms

Synonyms are words with **similar** meanings.

I feel **cold**.   Yes, it is a bit **chilly**.

Match up the pairs of words with similar meanings.

1. help — tiny
2. sly
3. small   foe
4. stop   gather
5. enemy   aid
6. moan   complain
7. assemble   within
8. remedy   miserable
9. inside   crafty
10. difficult   ill
11. sick   prevent
12. broad   wide
13. quick   crazy
14. sad   cure
15. mad   fast

hard

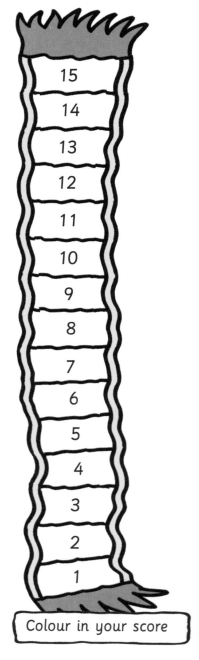

15
14
13
12
11
10
9
8
7
6
5
4
3
2
1

Colour in your score

Test 2 Direct and reported speech

We can write speech in two ways – as **direct speech** or **reported speech**.

The girl said, "My shoes are new."

This is **direct speech**. The girl's exact words are inside speech marks.

The girl said that her shoes were new.

This is **reported speech**. The girl's exact words are not used. Speech marks are not used either.

Write if each sentence uses direct or reported speech.

1. "I will dig the garden," Mr Jones said. _____

2. The man said that he didn't do it. _____

3. The boy shouted that he was hurt. _____

4. "My aunt is coming soon," Anna said. _____

5. She shouted, "Leave me alone!" _____

6. The lady asked if she could have some apples. _____

7. "Who lives here?" Ian asked. _____

8. Mark said that he was going on holiday. _____

9. The girl said that she wasn't ready yet. _____

10. "Be quiet," Emma whispered. _____

11. "The corn is ripe," the farmer said. _____

12. Sam boasted that he could climb the tree. _____

13. "I'm ten," Edward said. _____

14. The child said that she knew the answer. _____

15. "Did you watch TV last night?" Vikram asked. _____

Colour in your score

Test 2

Test 3 Common expressions

We use many **common expressions** in our language. Sometimes they are a little hard to understand.

For example, we say that when you give away a secret you **let the cat out of the bag**!

Choose the correct word to complete each common expression.

1. to have an _____ to grind (anvil/axe)

2. to hit below the _____ (belt/neck)

3. to take the _____ by the horns (bull/devil)

4. to put the _____ before the horse (apple/cart)

5. to be sent to _____ (Cambridge/Coventry)

6. to sit on the _____ (wall/fence)

7. to play second _____ (fiddle/string)

8. to bury the _____ (hatchet/hammer)

9. to strike while the _____ is hot (weather/iron)

10. to turn over a new _____ (penny/leaf)

11. to make a _____ out of a molehill (meal/mountain)

12. to face the _____ (music/front)

13. to smell a _____ (rat/dustbin)

14. to blow your own _____ (horn/trumpet)

15. to get into hot _____ (air/water)

Colour in your score

Test 3

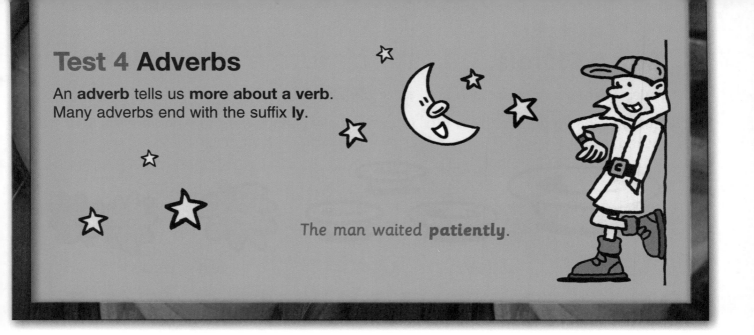

Test 4 Adverbs

An **adverb** tells us **more about a verb**.
Many adverbs end with the suffix **ly**.

The man waited **patiently**.

**Make each of these adjectives into adverbs ending in ly.
Take care with the spelling.**

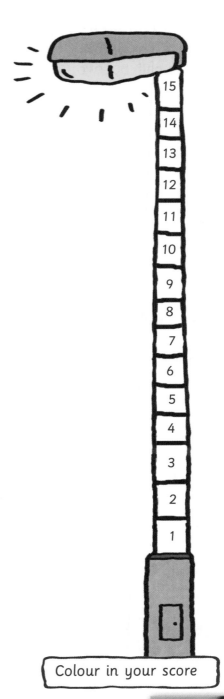

1. clever   _____

2. poor   _____

3. hungry   _____

4. simple   _____

5. grateful   _____

6. lucky   _____

7. heavy   _____

8. idle   _____

9. patient   _____

10. merry   _____

11. equal   _____

12. feeble   _____

13. fatal   _____

14. loyal   _____

15. lazy   _____

Colour in your score

Test 4

Test 5 Plurals

Rule 1: When a noun ends in **s**, **x**, **sh** or **ch**, we add **es** to make it plural.

Rule 2: When a noun ends in **f** (or **fe**), we usually change the **f** to **v** and add **es** to make it plural.

dish – dishes   leaf – leaves

Fill in the correct noun to complete each of these.

1. one calf, but two _____

2. one watch, but two _____

3. one loaf, but two _____

4. one brush, but two _____

5. one fox, but two _____

6. one shelf, but two _____

7. one wife, but two _____

8. one boss, but two _____

9. one _____, but two knives

10. one _____, but two boxes

11. one _____, but two wolves

12. one _____, but two glasses

13. one _____, but two branches

14. one _____, but two halves

15. one _____, but two wishes

Colour in your score

Test 6 Joining sentences

Two sentences may often be made into one sentence by using a **conjunction** (a **joining** word).

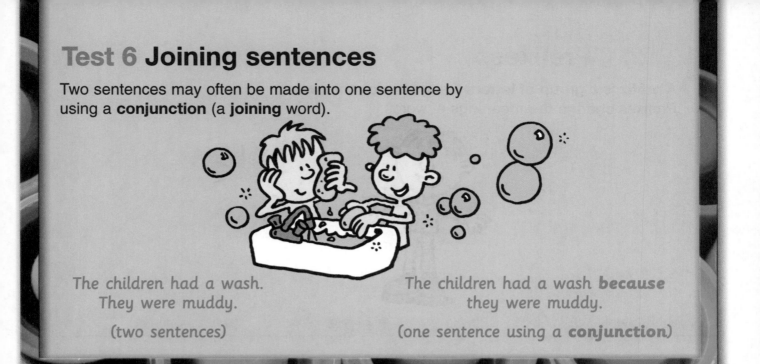

The children had a wash.
They were muddy.

(two sentences)

The children had a wash **because**
they were muddy.

(one sentence using a **conjunction**)

<u>Underline</u> the conjunction in each sentence.

1. John is a good swimmer but he is no good at drawing.

2. I like apples because they are sweet.

3. I saved my money so I could buy a toy.

4. I stayed out until it was dark.

5. I turned off the TV because I wanted to read.

6. It got too hot so I had a swim.

7. I was happy when I won the race.

8. I stopped at the kerb before I crossed the road.

9. My uncle gives me a present whenever he comes.

10. It started to rain after we went indoors.

11. I ran home so I could have my tea.

12. I got low marks although I tried hard.

13. Winter is nice but summer is better.

14. The leaves began to fall because it was autumn.

15. We watch TV when we get home.

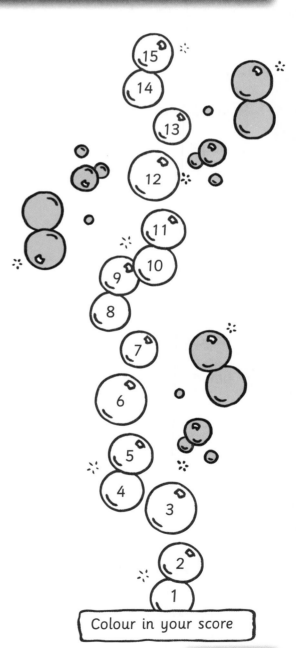

Colour in your score

Test 6

Test 7 Prefixes

A **prefix** is a **group of letters** that go **in front** of a word.
Prefixes **change the meanings** of words.

visible   invisible

Take the prefix off each of these words. Write the
root word you are left with.

1. impatient _____

2. irresponsible _____

3. illegal _____

4. incapable _____

5. postcode _____

6. recall _____

7. triangle _____

8. deport _____

9. beside _____

10. encircle _____

11. exchange _____

12. interact _____

13. midnight _____

14. nonsense _____

15. overbalance _____

Colour in your score

Test 7

Test 8 Auxiliary verbs

Sometimes a verb needs a **helper** (or **auxiliary**) verb to help it make sense.

Some children **were** climbing the tree.

Choose the best auxiliary verb to complete each sentence.

1. Tom _____ looking in the shop window.   (is/are)

2. The girls _____ playing netball.   (is/are)

3. A car _____ speeding down the road.   (was/were)

4. The toads _____ croaking loudly.   (was/were)

5. I _____ going home.   (am/are)

6. We _____ approaching London.   (am/are)

7. I _____ whistle.   (can/has)

8. I _____ like to go if possible.   (would/could)

9. _____ you think you can run that fast?   (Do/Does)

10. Why _____ the sun set?   (do/does)

11. We _____ sail tomorrow.   (are/will)

12. What _____ the robber steal?   (did/do)

13. Next week I _____ going to the seaside.   (am/will)

14. Ben _____ not score a goal.   (do/did)

15. I _____ been to Coventry.   (has/have)

15
14
13
12
11
10
9
8
7
6
5
4
3
2
1

Colour in your score

Test 8

Test 9 Suffixes

A **suffix** is a **group of letters** that can be added to the **end** of a word to **change its meaning** or the **way it is used**.

When we perform something we give a performance.

perform – perform**ance**

Match up the pairs of words with the same suffixes.

1.	treatment	collection
2.	assistant	disturbance
3.	action	punishment
4.	artist	interference
5.	appearance	attendant
6.	arrival	pressure
7.	justice	cyclist
8.	confidence	approval
9.	marriage	wisdom
10.	pleasure	service
11.	darkness	visitor
12.	childhood	blindness
13.	conductor	carriage
14.	discovery	parenthood
15.	kingdom	bakery

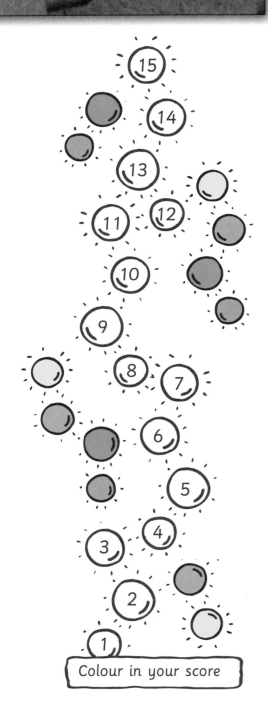

Colour in your score

Test 9

Test 10 Verb tenses

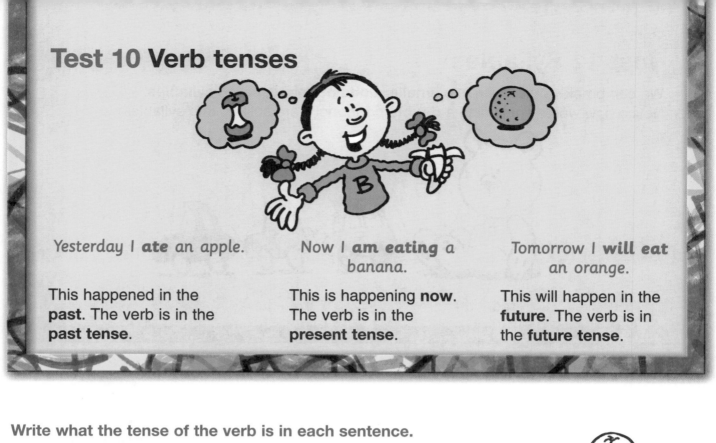

Yesterday I **ate** an apple.

Now I **am eating** a banana.

Tomorrow I **will eat** an orange.

This happened in the **past**. The verb is in the **past tense**.

This is happening **now**. The verb is in the **present tense**.

This will happen in the **future**. The verb is in the **future tense**.

Write what the tense of the verb is in each sentence.

1. Yesterday I fell over. _____

2. In the future we will travel in spaceships. _____

3. I am swimming in the lake. _____

4. Some birds are singing outside my window. _____

5. Tomorrow it will be my birthday. _____

6. In 1666 there was a great fire in London. _____

7. Laura drank a cup of tea. _____

8. Mr Shaw is mowing the lawn. _____

9. Will Scott win the cup? _____

10. Who is driving that car? _____

11. The man chopped down the tree. _____

12. I am going on a plane tomorrow. _____

13. Will it be sunny in the morning? _____

14. Last night I snored in bed. _____

15. Sarah is having a bath. _____

15 14 13 12 11 10 9 8 7 6 5 4 3 2 1

Colour in your score

Test 10

Test 11 Syllables

We can break words down into **smaller units of sound**, called **syllables**.
Notice how words containing a **double consonant** are split up into syllables.

ted - dy   traf - fic

Split these words into two syllables.

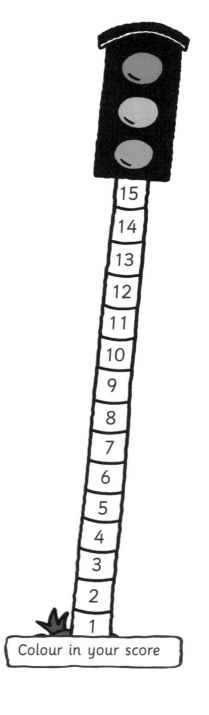

1. barrow _____ bar - row _____

2. berry _____

3. pillow _____

4. dinner _____

5. rabbit _____

6. sadder _____

7. muffle _____

8. wriggle _____

9. slimming _____

10. puppet _____

11. assist _____

12. batted _____

13. dazzle _____

14. cabbage _____

15. office _____

15
14
13
12
11
10
9
8
7
6
5
4
3
2
1

Colour in your score

Test 11

Test 12 Common letter strings

Some words with the **same letter strings** are pronounced **differently**.

There are **mice** in the **office**.

Underline the odd word out in each set.

1. paddle   saddle   waddle

2. ball   call   shall

3. starter   quarter   charter

4. meat   beat   great

5. wear   near   year

6. here   there   where

7. what   chat   that

8. mice   nice   office

9. stamp   camp   swamp

10. shine   fine   engine

11. flower   lower   slower

12. home   some   dome

13. good   wood   flood

14. rose   nose   lose

15. touch   couch   pouch

15
14
13
12
11
10
9
8
7
6
5
4
3
2
1

Colour in your score

Test 12

Test 13 Subject/verb agreement

The **subject** and **verb** in each sentence must **agree** with each other.

The hens **were** clucking.

Choose the correct form of the verb to agree with the subject in each sentence.

1. We _____ eating our dinner. (was/were)

2. We _____ it last week. (done/did)

3. The boy _____ making a model. (is/are)

4. The children _____ shouting. (is/are)

5. A spider _____ eight legs. (has/have)

6. Snakes _____ through grass. (slide/slides)

7. Ben _____ to wear jeans. (like/likes)

8. History _____ my favourite subject. (is/are)

9. I _____ my dinner. (want/wants)

10. _____ you at home last night? (Was/Were)

11. The price of the toy _____ too high. (is/are)

12. Children _____ to school every day. (go/goes)

13. Each of the apples _____ bad. (is/are)

14. Fish and chips _____ a popular meal. (is/are)

15. The number of cars _____ increasing. (is/are)

Colour in your score

Test 13

Onomatopoeia is when the **sound** of the word is **similar** to the **sound** of the thing it describes.

Tick

a clock **ticks**

Choose the word which best describes each sound.

1. the _____ of a bell   (clang/rattle)

2. the _____ of a trumpet   (beep/blare)

3. the _____ of raindrops   (patter/crunch)

4. the _____ of leaves   (rumble/rustle)

5. the _____ of brakes   (swish/screech)

6. the _____ of a hinge   (creak/click)

7. the _____ of a siren   (howl/wail)

8. the _____ of steam   (hiss/shuffle)

9. the _____ of an engine   (clang/chug)

10. the _____ of coins   (chime/chink)

11. the _____ of a drum   (pop/beat)

12. the _____ of an explosion   (blast/ping)

13. the _____ of water down a drain   (giggle/gurgle)

14. the _____ of dishes   (chatter/clatter)

15. the _____ of the wind   (shifting/sighing)

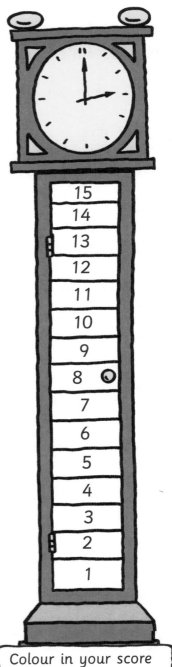

15
14
13
12
11
10
9
8
7
6
5
4
3
2
1

Colour in your score

Test 14

Test 15 Homophones

Homophones are words that **sound the same** but are **spelt differently**.

*The boat with the torn **sail** was for **sale**.*

Choose the correct word to complete each sentence.

1. The brown _____ loved honey.   (bare/bear)

2. I have _____ a lot recently.   (groan/grown)

3. The _____ had large antlers.   (dear/deer)

4. Do _____ to me soon.   (write/right)

5. You need _____ to make cakes.   (flower/flour)

6. I paid my _____ and got off the bus.   (fare/fair)

7. The _____ was soft and ripe.   (pear/pair)

8. _____ is a type of meat.   (Stake/Steak)

9. We went for a _____ on a yacht.   (crews/cruise)

10. A _____ is found under a house.   (cellar/seller)

11. I had to _____ some cheese.   (grate/great)

12. An _____ is a small island.   (aisle/isle)

13. Another word for rough is _____.   (coarse/course)

14. Cornflakes is a breakfast _____.   (cereal/serial)

15. The soldier won a _____.   (medal/meddle)

Colour in your score

Test 15

Test 16 **Soft c and g**

When the letter **c** is followed by **e**, **i** or **y**, it makes an **s** sound.

When the letter **g** is followed by **e**, **i** or **y**, it makes a **j** sound.

a prince with a genie

Choose c or g to complete each of these words.

1. _____ity

2. stran_____e

3. _____entle

4. dan_____e

5. _____entre

6. pen_____e

7. _____iant

8. avera_____e

9. _____enerous

10. differen_____e

11. _____ertain

12. intelli_____ent

13. _____ircus

14. medi_____ine

15. ener_____y

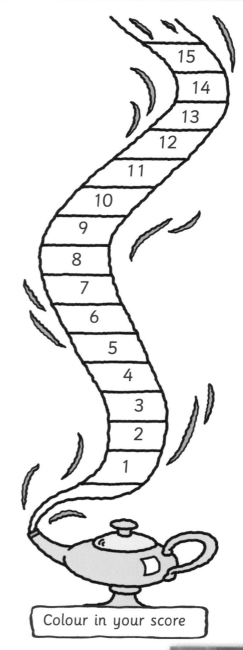

15
14
13
12
11
10
9
8
7
6
5
4
3
2
1

Colour in your score

Test 16

Test 17 Antonyms

An **antonym** is a word which has the **opposite** meaning.
Sometimes it can be made by adding a **prefix**.

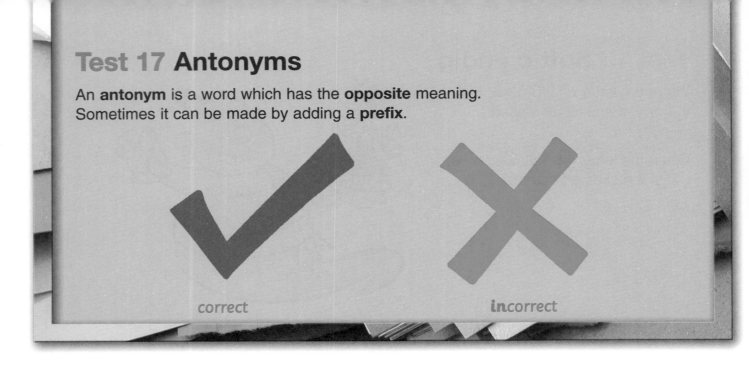

correct   **in**correct

Choose the correct prefix to give each word the opposite meaning.

1. _____ safe   (un/dis)

2. _____ behave   (im/mis)

3. _____ obey   (un/dis)

4. _____ selfish   (non/un)

5. _____ patient   (in/im)

6. _____ sane   (in/im)

7. _____ sense   (un/non)

8. _____ polite   (un/im)

9. _____ regular   (il/ir)

10. _____ logical   (il/ir)

11. _____ noble   (il/ig)

12. _____ pure   (in/im)

13. _____ lock   (in/un)

14. _____ loyal   (dis/mis)

15. _____ normal   (ab/un)

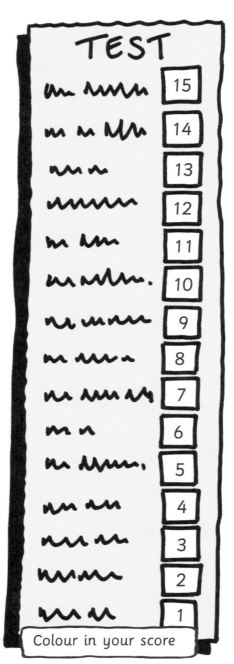

TEST

| 15 |
| 14 |
| 13 |
| 12 |
| 11 |
| 10 |
| 9 |
| 8 |
| 7 |
| 6 |
| 5 |
| 4 |
| 3 |
| 2 |
| 1 |

Colour in your score

Test 17

Test 18 Doubling the consonant

When a verb ends with a **single consonant** preceded by a **short vowel**, we have to **double the consonant** before adding the suffix **ing** or **ed**.

rob ⟶ robbing ⟶ robbed

Add the suffix ing to these verbs.

1. tap   _____

2. jog   _____

3. hug   _____

4. ban   _____

5. begin   _____

Add the suffix ed to these verbs.

6. nod   _____

7. pop   _____

8. wag   _____

9. chat   _____

10. travel   _____

Take the suffix off the verb. Write the root verb you are left with.

11. shopping   _____

12. mugged _____

13. ripped   _____

14. stopping   _____

15. grabbed   _____

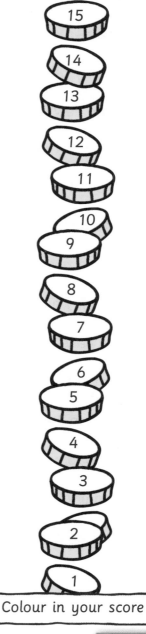

Colour in your score

Test 18

Test 19 Making it clear

Sometimes the meanings of words can be **ambiguous** (unclear). We have to use the context of the sentence to work them out.

An elephant lifts its trunk.

<u>Underline</u> the meaning of the word in bold in each sentence.

1. My **trainer** was muddy.   (someone who coaches/you wear it on your foot)

2. I wore my **glasses**.   (you drink from them/you wear them to help you see)

3. The **bat** flew near me.   (you hit a ball with it/a mouse-like flying creature)

4. There was a **tap** on the door.   (you turn it on/someone knocking)

5. I looked at my **palm**.   (a type of tree/part of your hand)

6. The man lit his **pipe**.   (a tube water goes through/something you smoke)

7. There's a **fork** in the road.   (you eat with it/where a road divides into two)

8. The **bark** was brown.   (the sound a dog makes/you find it on tree trunks)

9. I put a case in the **boot**.   (part of a car/something you wear on your foot)

10. I bit my **nail**.   (you hit it with a hammer/part of a finger)

11. I played in the **match**.   (a game/used for lighting fires)

12. The sheep was in a **pen**.   (something to write with/an enclosure for animals)

13. The squirrel ate a **nut**.   (a metal bolt/it grows on trees)

14. There was a lot of **junk**.   (a Chinese ship/rubbish)

15. I ate a **date**.   (a type of fruit/a specific time)

15
14
13
12
11
10
9
8
7
6
5
4
3
2
1

Colour in your score

Test 19

Test 20 Standard English

Standard English is the kind of language used in education, government and business.

Me and Sarah have been shopping. ☒

This is not grammatically correct.

Sarah and I have been shopping. ☑

This is how it is written in Standard English.

Correct the underlined word in each of these sentences.

1. I saw the man ~~what~~ did it. _____who_____

2. We didn't have <u>no</u> money. _____

3. He <u>done</u> it yesterday. _____

4. They could <u>of</u> done it easily. _____

5. I <u>ain't</u> going. _____

6. The man didn't say <u>nothing</u>. _____

7. We <u>seen</u> the cat up the tree. _____

8. The books <u>wasn't</u> in my desk. _____

9. Do you <u>wanna</u> sweet? _____

10. All of the children <u>was</u> dirty. _____

11. He should have <u>took</u> more notice. _____

12. He doesn't come here <u>no</u> more. _____

13. Who has taken <u>me</u> socks? _____

14. That's <u>real</u> terrible. _____

15. I don't want <u>no</u> crisps _____

Colour in your score

Test 20

Test 21 Unstressed vowels

When we say some words it is **hard to hear** some of the vowels.
These are called **unstressed vowels**.

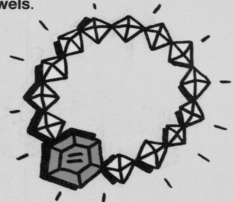

a diamond necklace

Fill in the missing unstressed vowel in each word.

1. usu____l

2. capt____in

3. veg____table

4. cam____ra

5. int____rest

6. libr____ry

7. temp____rature

8. diff____rent

9. bus____ness

10. secr____tary

11. valu____ble

12. parl____ament

13. hist____ry

14. sign____ture

15. nurs____ry

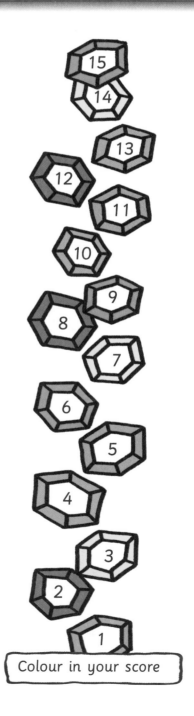

Colour in your score

Test 21

Test 22 Verbs ending with e

When a verb ends with a **magic e**, we usually drop the **e** before we add the suffix **ing** or **ed**.

bake → baking → baked

Yesterday I baked a cake.   Today I am baking some bread.

Add the suffix ing to these verbs.

1. rule _____

2. mope _____

3. dine _____

4. gape _____

5. bite _____

Add the suffix ed to these verbs.

6. rake _____

7. chime _____

8. hope _____

9. use _____

10. choke _____

Take the suffix off these verbs. Write the root verb you are left with.

11. excusing _____

12. sloping _____

13. shining _____

14. forgiving _____

15. mistaking _____

Colour in your score

Test 22

Test 23 Double negatives

This baby hasn't got no teeth. ☒

This sentence contains a **double negative**.

This baby hasn't got any teeth. ☑

This sentence is written **correctly**.

Change these sentences to make them correct.

1. There aren't ~~no~~ sweets left.   _____any_____ any

2. I didn't go ~~nowhere~~ yesterday.   _____

3. I haven't ~~never~~ been to Spain.   _____

4. The boy said he didn't see ~~nobody~~.   _____

5. The car wasn't ~~nowhere~~ near the accident.   _____

6. I don't want ~~no~~ trouble.   _____

7. I can't find the book ~~nowhere~~.   _____

8. There isn't ~~no~~ point in arguing.   _____

9. The bike hasn't got ~~no~~ tyres.   _____

10. I didn't tell ~~no-one~~.   _____

11. I didn't say ~~nothing~~.   _____

12. I haven't ~~never~~ tasted mangoes.   _____

13. The thief wasn't ~~nowhere~~ to be seen.   _____

14. I didn't do ~~nothing~~ wrong.   _____

15. I haven't got ~~no~~ money.   _____

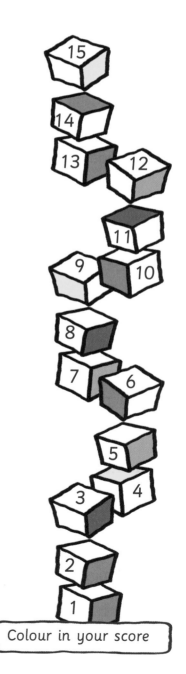

Colour in your score

Test 23

Test 24 Sentences and phrases

The girl watched TV with her friend.

A **sentence** contains a **verb**.
It **makes sense** on its own.

with her friend

A **phrase** does **not** contain a verb.
It does **not** make sense on its own.

Write whether each of these is a sentence or a phrase.

1. A rabbit scampers. _____

2. in the morning _____

3. green and black _____

4. Yesterday Geeta passed her test. _____

5. I did my homework when I got home. _____

6. with neat handwriting _____

7. The car was left in the garage. _____

8. until Tuesday _____

9. My foot got stuck in the mud. _____

10. through the woods _____

11. because of the noise _____

12. The robber stole the jewels. _____

13. Some sparrows were looking for worms. _____

14. a loud banging noise _____

15. The rain fell heavily during the night. _____

Colour in your score

Test 24

Test 25 Clauses

A **clause** is a **group of words** which can be used as a **whole sentence** or as **part of a sentence**. A clause must contain a **verb** and a **subject**.

Tom kicked the ball.
subject   verb

This is a **one-clause** sentence.

Underline the subject of each of these one-clause sentences.

1. Anna ate an apple.   (Anna/apple)

2. The farmer ploughed the field.   (farmer/field)

3. The chicken laid an egg.   (chicken/egg)

4. Bees live in hives.   (bees/hives)

5. Out of the door came Sam.   (door/Sam)

6. Through the wood came the dragon.   (wood/dragon)

7. We saw a dog in the park.   (we/dog)

8. The brave knight fell off the horse.   (knight/horse)

9. I wrote a long story.   (I/story)

10. The alien spoke a strange alien language.   (alien/language)

11. Suddenly a frog hopped past me.   (frog/me)

12. Rob likes sweets.   (Rob/sweets)

13. After the goal the crowd roared.   (goal/crowd)

14. Rockets fly in space.   (rockets/space)

15. In came the clowns with funny hats.   (clowns/hats)

Colour in your score

Test 25

Test 26 Prepositions

A **preposition** tells us the **position** of one thing in relation to another.

*The builder climbed **up** the ladder.*

Choose the best preposition to complete each sentence.

1. We stared _____ the strange sight. (by/at)

2. The fox walked _____ the woods. (through/beyond)

3. A tree was blown down _____ the storm. (during/until)

4. The man ran away _____ the fire. (off/from)

5. The dog jumped _____ the wall. (of/over)

6. I dropped a coin _____ the well. (before/down)

7. Don't mess about _____ electricity. (with/among)

8. I was thrilled _____ my present. (to/with)

9. The swimmer dived _____ the pool. (in/into)

10. The parade drove _____ the crowds. (against/past)

11. The train went _____ the bridge. (up/under)

12. Emma hid _____ a tree. (down/behind)

13. Tom stood _____ Sam and Ben. (through/between)

14. I pushed _____ the closed door. (against/for)

15. I fell _____ the wall. (up/off)

15
14
13
12
11
10
9
8
7
6
5
4
3
2
1

Colour in your score

Test 26

Test 27 Punctuation

Punctuation marks help the
reader **make sense of a text**.

Mr Smith said what a nasty day X

This is not punctuated.

Mr Smith said, "What a nasty day!" ☑

This is punctuated. It is easier to read.

Fill in the missing punctuation mark in each sentence.

1. The sun went behind a cloud___

2. The man asked___ "Is it a nice day?"

3. What is the capital of Mexico___

4. It's not fair___

5. I___ve tried very hard.

6. "My dog is called Spot,___ Anna said.

7. After a while___ the queen appeared.

8. I saw a car, a bus___ a lorry and a bike.

9. The man said, ___Come with me."

10. "Pass the salt, Ben___" Mrs Jones said.

11. Yes___ it is my coat.

12. Don___t talk while you are eating.

13. Curry was Edward___s favourite food.

14. The girl shrieked, "I'm drowning___"

15. The car, a red sports car___ raced past.

Colour in your score

Test 27

Test 28 Apostrophes for possession

We use **apostrophes** to show who or what something **belongs to**.

the man's hat

(the hat belonging to the man)

We add **'s** when there is only **one** owner.

the squirrels' nuts

(the nuts belonging to the squirrels)

We usually add **'** **after the s** if there is **more than one** owner.

Rewrite each phrase. Use the apostrophe correctly.

1. the apple belonging to the girl _____

2. the bike belonging to the boy _____

3. the car belonging to the doctor _____

4. the tools belonging to the builder _____

5. the hutch belonging to the rabbits _____

6. the purse belonging to Anna _____

7. the hats belonging to the soldiers _____

8. the lead belonging to the dog _____

9. the bags belonging to the ladies _____

10. the rocket belonging to the aliens _____

11. the house belonging to Mrs Shaw _____

12. the ship belonging to the sailors _____

13. the egg belonging to the bird _____

14. the toys belonging to the babies _____

15. the shell belonging to the snail _____

15
14
13
12
11
10
9
8
7
6
5
4
3
2
1

Colour in your score

Test 28

Test 29 Making new words

We can sometimes **modify** a **root word** and turn it into a different **class of word**.

We can change some nouns into adjectives.

accident (a noun) – ***accidental*** (an adjective)

Match up the adjectives which come from each noun.

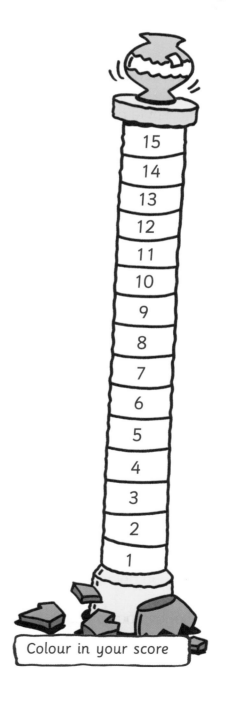

1. fashion   criminal

2. fool   responsible

3. giant   foolish

4. crime   heroic

5. danger   fashionable

6. expense   comfortable

7. hero   childish

8. fable   merciful

9. child   volcanic

10. friend   gigantic

11. mercy   woollen

12. response   expensive

13. comfort   fabulous

14. volcano   friendly

15. wool   dangerous

Colour in your score

15
14
13
12
11
10
9
8
7
6
5
4
3
2
1

Test 29

Test 30 Connecting clauses together

We sometimes use a **conjunction** (a **joining** word) to join two clauses together.

*I eat lots of apples **because** they are so nice.*

Choose the best conjunction to join the two clauses together.

1. I like climbing trees _____ I can hide.   (so/but)

2. I got angry _____ my friend upset me.   (if/when)

3. We go swimming _____ we can.   (and/whenever)

4. I went to bed _____ I ate my dinner.   (after/and)

5. I did it _____ I didn't want to.   (so/although)

6. I washed quickly _____ I was going out.   (because/when)

7. I read a book _____ I had tea.   (but/before)

8. Tom likes Kerry _____ Kerry doesn't like Tom.   (and/but)

9. I could not go out _____ I finished my spellings.   (until/because)

10. I get annoyed _____ my sister pushes me.   (whenever/so)

11. I like swimming _____ it is good for me.   (because/after)

12. It got dark _____ I went home.   (so/but)

13. Ben likes football _____ enjoys playing cards.   (when/and)

14. Don't cross _____ the road is clear.   (if/until)

15. I would go _____ I was allowed to.   (so/if)

15
14
13
12
11
10
9
8
7
6
5
4
3
2
1

Colour in your score

Test 30

ANSWERS

Test 1
1. aid
2. crafty
3. tiny
4. prevent
5. foe
6. complain
7. gather
8. cure
9. within
10. hard
11. ill
12. wide
13. fast
14. miserable
15. crazy

Test 2
1. direct
2. reported
3. reported
4. direct
5. direct
6. reported
7. direct
8. reported
9. reported
10. direct
11. direct
12. reported
13. direct
14. reported
15. direct

Test 3
1. axe
2. belt
3. bull
4. cart
5. Coventry
6. fence
7. fiddle
8. hatchet
9. iron
10. leaf
11. mountain
12. music
13. rat
14. trumpet
15. water

Test 4
1. cleverly
2. poorly
3. hungrily
4. simply
5. gratefully
6. luckily
7. heavily
8. idly
9. patiently
10. merrily
11. equally
12. feebly
13. fatally
14. loyally
15. lazily

Test 5
1. calves
2. watches
3. loaves
4. brushes
5. foxes
6. shelves
7. wives
8. bosses
9. knife
10. box
11. wolf
12. glass
13. branch
14. half
15. wish

Test 6
1. but
2. because
3. so
4. until
5. because
6. so
7. when
8. before
9. whenever
10. after
11. so
12. although
13. but
14. because
15. when

Test 7
1. patient
2. responsible
3. legal
4. capable
5. code
6. call
7. angle
8. port
9. side
10. circle
11. change
12. act
13. night
14. sense
15. balance

Test 8
1. is
2. are
3. was
4. were
5. am
6. are
7. can
8. would
9. Do
10. does
11. will
12. did
13. am
14. did
15. have

Test 9
1. punishment
2. attendant
3. collection
4. cyclist
5. disturbance
6. approval
7. service
8. interference
9. carriage
10. pressure
11. blindness
12. parenthood
13. visitor
14. bakery
15. wisdom

Test 10
1. past
2. future
3. present
4. present
5. future
6. past
7. past
8. present
9. future
10. present
11. past
12. future
13. future
14. past
15. present

Test 11
1. bar - row
2. ber - ry
3. pil - low
4. din - ner
5. rab - bit
6. sad - der
7. muf - fle
8. wrig - gle
9. slim - ming
10. pup - pet
11. as - sist
12. bat - ted
13. daz - zle
14. cab - bage
15. of - fice

Test 12
1. waddle
2. shall
3. quarter
4. great
5. wear
6. here
7. what
8. office
9. swamp
10. engine
11. flower
12. some
13. flood
14. lose
15. touch

Test 13
1. were
2. did
3. is
4. are
5. has
6. slide
7. likes
8. is
9. want
10. Were
11. is
12. go
13. is
14. is
15. is

Test 14
1. clang
2. blare
3. patter
4. rustle
5. screech
6. creak
7. wail
8. hiss
9. chug
10. chink
11. beat
12. blast
13. gurgle
14. clatter
15. sighing

Test 15
1. bear
2. grown
3. deer
4. write
5. flour
6. fare
7. pear
8. Steak
9. cruise
10. cellar
11. grate
12. isle
13. coarse
14. cereal
15. medal

Test 16
The missing letters are in **bold**.
1. ci**t**y
2. stran**g**e
3. **g**entle
4. dan**c**e
5. **c**entre
6. pen**c**e
7. **g**iant
8. avera**g**e
9. **g**enerous
10. differen**c**e
11. **c**ertain
12. intelli**g**ent
13. **c**ircus
14. medi**c**ine
15. ener**g**y

Test 17
The missing prefixes are in **bold**.
1. **un**safe
2. **mis**behave
3. **dis**obey
4. **un**selfish
5. **im**patient
6. **in**sane
7. **non**sense
8. **im**polite
9. **ir**regular
10. **il**logical
11. **ig**noble
12. **im**pure
13. **un**lock
14. **dis**loyal
15. **ab**normal